# Real-World Problem Solving

## Graphic Novels

**BOOK 1**

**Glencoe**

New York, New York
Columbus, Ohio
Chicago, Illinois
Woodland Hills, California

**Illustrators:** *Greg Lawhun, Wayno, Michael McParlane, Mark Ricketts, Shane McDermott, Joel Priddy, Scott Rolfs, Pat Lewis, Jim Callahan*

 **Glencoe**

The **McGraw·Hill** Companies

Send all inquiries to:

Glencoe/McGraw-Hill
8787 Orion Place
Columbus, OH 43240-4027

ISBN: 978-0-07-878293-0
MHID: 0-07-878293-7

Printed in the United States of America.

10   MAL 15 14 13 12 11 10

# TABLE of CONTENTS

# LETTER to the TEACHER

## USING GRAPHIC NOVELS:
### Popular Culture and Mathematics Interact

Graphic novels represent a significant segment of the literary market for adolescents and young adults. They are amazingly diverse, both in terms of their content and usefulness. Graphic novels are exactly what teens are looking for—they are motivating, engaging, challenging, and interesting. They allow teachers to enter the youth culture and students to bring their "out of school" experiences into the classroom.

Graphic novels have also been used effectively with students with disabilities, struggling readers, and English learners. One of the theories behind the use of graphic novels for struggling adolescents focuses on the fact that the graphic novel presents complex ideas that are interesting and engaging for adolescents, while reducing the text or reading demands.

However, graphic novels are motivating and engaging for *all* students. They allow us to differentiate our instruction and provide universal access to the curriculum. We hope you'll find the graphic novels in this book useful as you engage your students in the study of mathematics and problem-solving.

Sincerely,
Douglas Fisher & Nancy Frey

**Douglas Fisher, Ph.D.**
Professor
San Diego State University

**Nancy Frey, Ph.D.**
Associate Professor
San Diego State University

## Graphic Novels in the Classroom

As we have noted, graphic novels are an excellent adjunct text. While they cannot and should not replace reading or the core, standards-based textbook, they can be effectively used to build students' background knowledge, to motivate students, to provide a different access route to the content, and to allow students to check and review their work.

Mathematical problem solving is presented in graphic novel format. The novels contain real-world problems for each of the following mathematical content strands: Number Sense, Algebraic Thinking, Geometry, Measurement, Statistics and Probability, and Mathematical Reasoning.

- The first graphic novel that appears in each content strand describes a real-world problem that is solved in graphic novel format.

- The second and third graphic novels that appear in each content strand are left to the reader to formulate the solution.

- Finally, there are additional problems for students to practice on their own.

## Teaching Strategies

1. **Previewing Content** You can use a graphic novel as a lesson preview to activate background and prior knowledge. For example, you may display a graphic novel on the overhead projector and discuss it with the class. By doing so, you may provide students with advance information that they will read later in the book. Alternatively, you may display the graphic novel and invite students, in pairs or groups, to share their thinking with one another. Regardless of the approach, the goal is to activate students' interest and background knowledge in advance of the reading.

2. **Narrative Writing** Use the second and third graphic novels from each content strand and ask students to solve the posed problem in graphic novel format. Students should be encouraged to create character dialogue and complete the story line detailing their solution. Another alternative is to provide students with the first two pages of the first graphic novel and ask students to complete the story line with the solution to the problem posed. Not only does this engage students in thinking about the content, but it also provides you with some assessment information. Based on the dialogue that the students create of their solution, you'll understand what they already know, what they misunderstand, and what they do not yet know.

3. **Reviewing Content** In addition to narrative summaries, graphic novels can also be used for content review. While there are many reasons to review content—such as preparing for a test—graphic novels are especially useful for providing students with a review of past chapters. You can use a graphic novel from a previous chapter to review its major concepts.

4. **Analysis** In the analysis approach, students read the graphic novel to try to understand the main point the author is making. This approach is particularly useful after students have covered the content in their textbook. Encouraging students to pose questions about the text will help to uncover the main points. For example:

   • Why did the author choose this real-world situation to present this concept we have studied? What are some other real-world situations that can be used to present this concept?

   • What does the graphic novel tell me about this concept we have studied?

   Have students write a few sentences answering these questions. Then, have them summarize what they believe is the main point of the graphic novel.

5. **Visualizing** Have your students skim over the exercises in the chapter you are working on or the Practice On Your Own pages. The student should then pick one exercise and create their own graphic representation about it. Another option would be to use other forms of multimedia for their topic. Students could take pictures, make a computer slide-show presentation, make a video, or create a song.

These are just some of the many uses of graphic novels. As you introduce them into your class, you may discover more ways to use them to engage your students in a new method of learning while exercising the multiple literacies that your students already possess. We welcome you to the world of learning through graphic novels!

## References

Cary, S. (2004). Going graphic: *Comics at work in the multilingual classroom.* Portsmouth, NH: Heinemann.

Fisher, D., & Frey, N. (2004). *Improving adolescent literacy: Strategies at work.* Upper Saddle River, NJ: Merrill Education.

Frey, N., & Fisher, D. (2004). Using graphic novels, anime, and the Internet in an urban high school. *English Journal, 93*(3), 19–25.

Gorman, M. (2002). What teens want: Thirty graphic novels you can't live without. *School Library Journal, 48*(8), 42–47.

Schwarz, G. (2002a). Graphic novels for diverse needs: Engaging reluctant and curious readers. *ALAN Review, 30*(1), 54–57.

Schwarz, G. (2002b). Graphic novels for multiple literacies. *Journal of Adolescent & Adult Literacy, 46,* 262–265.

Schwarz, G. (2004). Graphic novels: Multiple cultures and multiple literacies. *Thinking Classroom, 5*(4), 17–24.

# Number Sense

### Order Rational Numbers: Hoops!, page 4

First, set up the ratios as fractions in order to compare them.

David made 9 out of 15 shots, so his ratio is $\frac{9}{15}$, or $\frac{3}{5}$. Yu-Jun made 14 out of 20 shots, so her ratio is $\frac{14}{20}$, or $\frac{7}{10}$. Tyrell made 12 out of 18 shots, so his ratio is $\frac{12}{18}$, or $\frac{2}{3}$.

To compare the fractions, rewrite them using a common denominator. The least common denominator for 3, 5, and 10 is 30.

David $\quad \frac{3}{5} = \frac{18}{30}$ (×6) $\qquad$ Yu-Jun $\quad \frac{7}{10} = \frac{21}{30}$ (×3)

Tyrell $\quad \frac{2}{3} = \frac{20}{30}$ (×10)

Since $\frac{21}{30} > \frac{20}{30} > \frac{18}{30}$, Yu-Jun had the greatest ratio of baskets made to shots taken. She gets to decide what movie they will see that evening.

### Subtract Fractions: Going the Distance!, page 5

To subtract $8\frac{2}{3}$ feet from $9\frac{1}{4}$ feet, rewrite each fraction using a common denominator.

$$9\frac{1}{4} \text{ feet} - 8\frac{2}{3} \text{ feet} = 9\frac{3}{12} \text{ feet} - 8\frac{8}{12} \text{ feet}$$

$$= 8\frac{15}{12} \text{ feet} - 8\frac{8}{12} \text{ feet} = \frac{7}{12} \text{ feet} \quad \text{Rename and subtract.}$$

Gregory jumped $\frac{7}{12}$ feet (or 7 inches) farther than Simona.

### Practice On Your Own, page 6

**1.** D　**2.** F　**3.** B　**4.** H　**5.** C　**6.** H　**7.** C　**8.** G

# Algebraic Thinking

## Ratios: Net Worth?, page 10

To find which competitor is advertising the better deal, set up two ratios. Then, compare their unit rates.

Honest Ernie's Hoops Booth advertises 3 basketballs for $5. As a ratio of cost to basketballs, this can be represented as $\frac{5}{3}$. Dividing 5 by 3 gives a result of 1 basketball for about $1.67.

B-Ball Bargains advertises 5 basketballs for $8. As a ratio of cost to basketballs, this can be represented as $\frac{8}{5}$. Dividing 8 by 5 gives a result of 1 basketball for $1.60.

Since $1.60 < $1.67, B-Ball Bargains is advertising the better deal.

## Use Ratios to Make Predictions: Crunching Numbers, page 11

Since a free movie theater pass is advertised to be placed in 1 out of every 6 boxes of cinnamon crunch snack bars, you can use a number cube to simulate this situation. Each toss of the number cube represents one trial of buying a box of crunch bars. Choose one number on the number cube to represent a box of cinnamon crunch bars containing a free movie pass. For example, let the number 1 represent a box containing a free movie pass. So, the numbers 2, 3, 4, 5, and 6 represent boxes that do not contain a free movie pass. Perform 20 trials. Sample results are shown below.

| 4 | 6 | 1 | 3 | 2 | 4 | 5 | 4 | 3 | 1 |
|---|---|---|---|---|---|---|---|---|---|
| 1 | 3 | 6 | 4 | 5 | 2 | 3 | 1 | 6 | 5 |

Since the number 1 came up 4 times out of 20, the experimental probability that a box of cinnamon crunch bars contained a free movie pass is $\frac{4}{20}$, or $\frac{1}{5}$.

You can set up and solve a proportion to find the number of boxes of snack bars needed to obtain three free movie passes.

one free movie pass $\longrightarrow$ $\frac{1}{5} = \frac{3}{x}$ $\longleftarrow$ three free movie passes
five boxes $\longrightarrow$ $\longleftarrow$ number of boxes needed

$$\overset{\times 3}{\frac{1}{5} = \frac{3}{x}}_{\times 3}$$

Think: $1 \times 3 = 3, 5 \times 3 = ?$

$$\frac{1}{5} = \frac{3}{15}$$   $5 \times 3 = 15$

So, according to these experimental results, the teens would need to buy 15 boxes of cinnamon crunch bars to obtain 3 free movie passes.

## Practice On Your Own, page 12

**1.** B   **2.** G   **3.** B   **4.** H   **5.** C   **6.** J   **7.** A

# Geometry

### Coordinate Plane: Meet Me There, page 16

Draw a coordinate plane with Harding Junior High located at the origin (0, 0). Each interval along the *x*-axis represents a city block east of the school and each interval along the *y*-axis represents a city block north of the school. Plot the coordinates (0, 0), (2, 1), (1, 4), (3, 8), (6, 5), and (7, 3) to visually see the relationships.

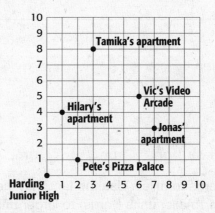

### Angles of Triangles: "Ladderal" Thinking, page 17

The teens do not have to climb the ladder to measure the angle at the top since two angles of the triangle are known: the right angle, 90°, and the angle that the ladder makes with the ground, 60°. Use the fact that all three angles in a triangle add to 180°. Let *x* represent the measure of the angle at the top of the triangle.

$$x° + 60° + \ 90° = \quad 180° \quad \text{Write the equation.}$$
$$x° + 150° = \quad 180° \quad \text{Add 60° and 90°.}$$
$$\underline{- 150° = - 150°} \quad \text{Subtract 150° from each side.}$$
$$x° \qquad = \quad 30°$$

Since the angle at the top is 30°, the ladder is not at a safe angle.

### Practice On Your Own, page 18

**1.** C    **2.** G    **3.** C    **4.** F    **5.** A    **6.** J

# Measurement

## Converting Customary Units: The Plane Facts, page 22

To convert feet to miles, first convert feet to yards. Use the fact that there are 3 feet in 1 yard. To change from smaller units (feet) to larger units (yards), divide 35,000 by 3.

$$
\begin{array}{r}
11{,}666\tfrac{2}{3} \\
3\overline{)35{,}000} \\
-3\phantom{5{,}000} \\
\hline
5\phantom{{,}000} \\
-3\phantom{{,}000} \\
\hline
20\phantom{00} \\
-18\phantom{00} \\
\hline
20\phantom{0} \\
-18\phantom{0} \\
\hline
20 \\
-18 \\
\hline
2
\end{array}
$$

So, 35,000 feet ≈ 11,667 yards.

Finally, convert 11,667 yards to miles. Use the fact that there are 1,760 yards in 1 mile. To change from smaller units (yards) to larger units (miles), divide 11,667 by 1,760.

$$
\begin{array}{r}
6.62 \\
1{,}760\overline{)11{,}667} \\
-10{,}560 \\
\hline
1{,}1070 \\
-1{,}0560 \\
\hline
5100 \\
-3520 \\
\hline
1580
\end{array}
$$

So, to the nearest tenth, 35,000 feet is approximately equal to 6.6 miles.

## Perimeter: The Sprinters, page 23

Since there are five apartment buildings along the length of the city block, and each apartment building is 30 feet in length, the length of the city block is 5 × 30, or 150 feet. Since there are five apartment buildings along the width of the city block, and each apartment building is 25 feet in width, the width of the city block is 5 × 25, or 125 feet. Use the formula for the perimeter of a rectangle, $P = 2\ell + 2w$, to find the perimeter of the entire city block, since the block is a rectangle.

| | |
|---|---|
| $P = 2\ell + 2w$ | Perimeter of a rectangle |
| $P = 2(150) + 2(125)$ | Replace $\ell$ with 150 and $w$ with 125. |
| $P = 300 + 250$ | Multiply. |
| $P = 550$ | Add. |

So, the perimeter of the entire city block is 550 feet.

## Practice On Your Own, page 24

**1.** C **2.** H **3.** D **4.** G **5.** C **6.** J **7.** B

# Statistics and Probability

## Probability: Rain or Shine, page 28

The probability that it will not rain on Wednesday is the complement of the probability that it will rain on Wednesday. The probability of an event and the probability of its complement add up to 100%. Since the probability that it will rain on Wednesday is 45%, we need to find the probability of the complement. To find the probability of the complement of 45%, subtract 45% from 100%.

Since 100% − 45% = 55%, the probability that it will not rain on Wednesday is 55%.

## Measures of Central Tendency: Riding the Line, page 29

To find the number of minutes the teens spent, on average, in line waiting for a ride, first find the sum of all the number of minutes spent waiting.

```
            30 minutes
            45 minutes
    1 hour
  + 1 hour  25 minutes
    2 hours 100 minutes
```

Rewrite 2 hours 100 minutes as 3 hours 40 minutes, since 100 minutes equals 1 hour 40 minutes.

The total time spent waiting in line was 3 hours 40 minutes, or 220 minutes. Divide this sum by the total number of rides, 4.

220 minutes ÷ 4 rides = 55 minutes per ride

So, on average, the teens spent 55 minutes in line waiting for a ride.

## Practice On Your Own, page 30

**1.** B    **2.** H    **3.** A    **4.** H    **5.** D    **6.** G

# Mathematical Reasoning

### Use Appropriate Units: Something Fishy, page 34

The volume of the tank represents how much water the fish tank can hold. Use the formula for the volume of a rectangular prism, $V = \ell wh$.

| | |
|---|---|
| $V = \ell wh$ | Volume of a rectangular prism |
| $V = 32 \times 15 \times 18$ | Replace $\ell$ with 32, $w$ with 15, and $h$ with 18. |
| $V = 8{,}640$ | Multiply. |

So, the volume of the fish tank is 8,640 in³. This means that the fish tank can hold 8,640 in³ of water.

The surface area of the tank represents how much glass was used to make the tank if all sides of the tank are covered with glass. Use the formula for the surface area of a rectangular prism, $S = 2\ell w + 2wh + 2\ell h$.

| | |
|---|---|
| $S = 2\ell w + 2wh + 2\ell h$ | Surface area of a rectangular prism |
| $S = 2(32)(15) + 2(32)(18) + 2(15)(18)$ | Replace $\ell$ with 32, $w$ with 15, and $h$ with 18. |
| $S = 2{,}652$ | Simplify. |

Since the top of the tank is open, there is only one surface, not two, consisting of glass with an area of $\ell w$, or 480 in².

So, the surface area of the fish tank is 2,652 − 480, or 2,172 in². This means that 2,172 in² of glass was used to make the fish tank.

### Solve a Simpler Problem: Party Time!, page 35

First, find the number of days in 12 years. Use the fact that there are approximately 365 days in 1 year. To change from a larger unit (years) to a smaller unit (days), find 365 × 12, or 4,380. So, there are approximately 4,380 days in 12 years.

Next, find the number of hours in 12 years. Use the fact that there are 24 hours in 1 day. To change from a larger unit (days) to a smaller unit (hours), multiply 4,380 by 24. Since 4,380 × 24 = 105,120, there are approximately 105,120 hours in 12 years.

Next, find the number of minutes in 12 years. Use the fact that there are 60 minutes in 1 hour. To change from a larger unit (hours) to a smaller unit (minutes), multiply 105,120 by 60. Since 105,120 × 60 = 6,307,200, there are approximately 6,307,200 minutes in 12 years.

Finally, find the number of seconds in 12 years. Use the fact that there are 60 seconds in 1 minute. To change from a larger unit (minutes) to a smaller unit (seconds), multiply 6,307,200 by 60. Since 6,307,200 × 60 = 378,432,000, there are approximately 378,432,000 seconds in 12 years.

### Practice On Your Own, page 36

**1.** B    **2.** H    **3.** D    **4.** G    **5.** B    **6.** H    **7.** A

## Trina, Kendra and Ramiro in
## KENDRA The TUTOR

**Do U tutor the Rollins kids 2nite or the Fords?**

TAP TAP TAP

**Trina wants to know where I'm tutoring.**

**Tell her about your options!**

**There R 3 Rollins kids. They pay $8 per hour per kid.**

TAP TAP

**I know the Fords have 2 kids. What do they pay U?**

TAP TAP TAP

**$10 per hour per kid until 8 p.m. $12 per hour per kid after 8 p.m.**

TAP TAP

**How long does each family want U 2 tutor?**

**She sure has a lot of questions!**

BZZZ

**Rollins: 5:30 to 8:30 p.m. Fords: 7 to 10 p.m.**

BZZZ

**For which family will U earn the most $$$?**

**Hey! Which one will pay me the most money?**

**I'm sure we can figure that out!**

BZZZ

## **Number Sense 3:** Subtract Fractions

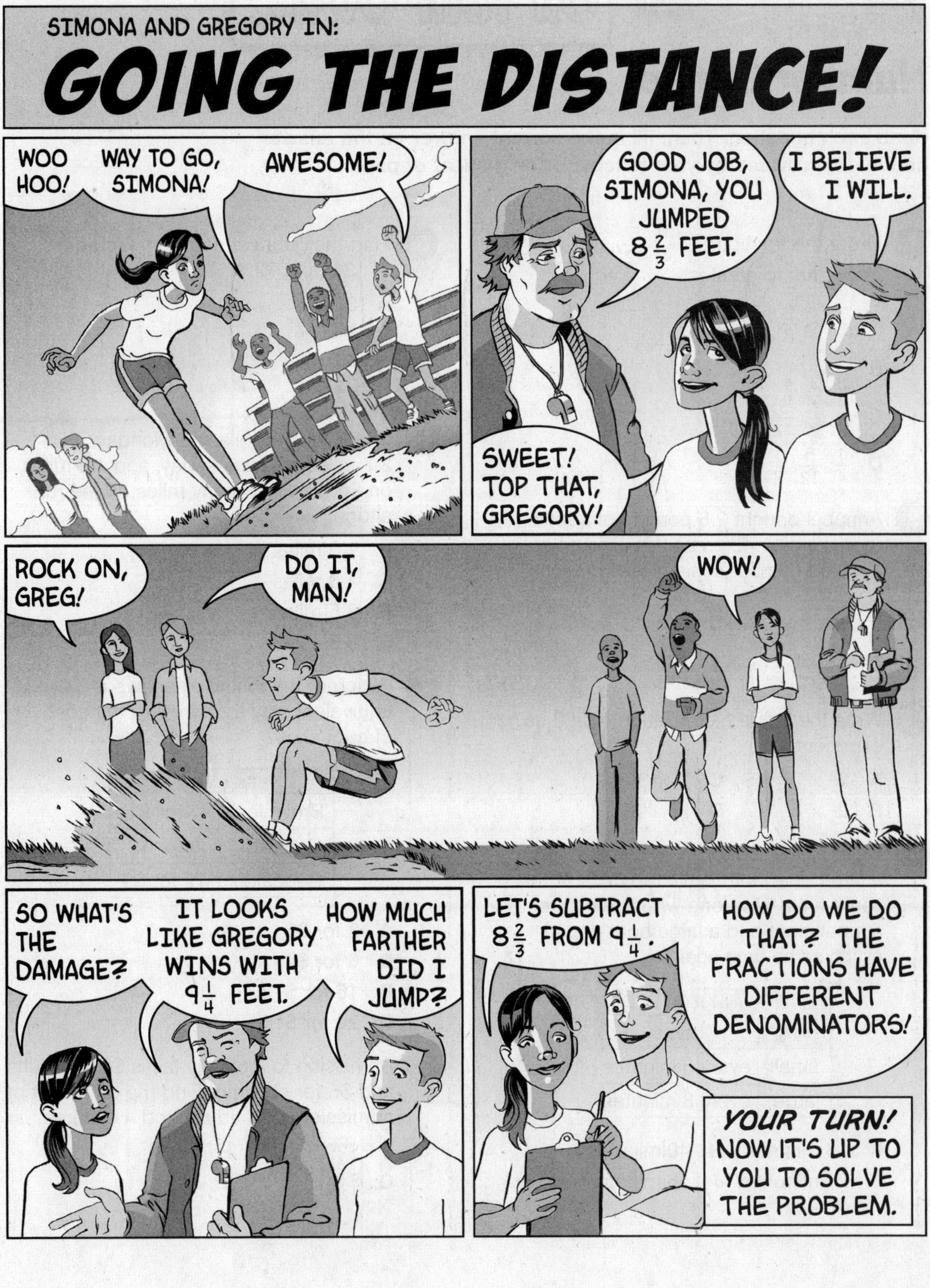

# Number Sense

Read each question. Then, fill in the correct answer on the answer document provided by your teacher or on a sheet of paper.

**1.** Order the fractions $\frac{2}{3}$, $\frac{1}{4}$, $\frac{5}{12}$, and $\frac{1}{2}$ from least to greatest.

A $\frac{1}{2}$, $\frac{1}{4}$, $\frac{2}{3}$, $\frac{5}{12}$

B $\frac{1}{2}$, $\frac{2}{3}$, $\frac{1}{4}$, $\frac{5}{12}$

C $\frac{2}{3}$, $\frac{1}{2}$, $\frac{5}{12}$, $\frac{1}{4}$

D $\frac{1}{4}$, $\frac{5}{12}$, $\frac{1}{2}$, $\frac{2}{3}$

**2.** Annabel bought 2.8 pounds of apples to make pies. Express this amount as a mixed number in simplest form.

F $2\frac{4}{5}$      H $2\frac{1}{2}$

G $2\frac{2}{3}$      J $2\frac{1}{8}$

**3.** Write the prime factorization of 252 using exponents.

A $2^2 \times 3^3 \times 5$    C $2 \times 3^2$

B $2^2 \times 3^2 \times 7$    D $2^3 \times 3$

**4.** Refer to the table. If a small boat and a large boat both leave the dock at the same time, how long will it be before a small boat and a large boat depart at the same time again?

| Water Ride | |
|---|---|
| **Boat** | **Departs** |
| small | every 5 minutes |
| large | every 8 minutes |

F 16 minutes    H 40 minutes

G 25 minutes    J 56 minutes

**5.** Find the greatest common factor of 27, 36, and 72.

A 3

B 6

C 9

D 12

**6.** Derek ran 1.6 miles on Monday, 2.7 miles on Wednesday, and 4.2 miles on Friday. How many miles did he run altogether?

F 7.3 miles

G 7.5 miles

H 8.5 miles

J 8.8 miles

**7.** Which of the following shows an equivalent way to represent the cost of cupcakes?

| Bake Sale | |
|---|---|
| Brownies | 3 for $1 |
| Cookies | 8 for $2 |
| Cupcakes | 12 for $9 |

A 8 for $5

B 6 for $4

C 16 for $12

D 20 for $16

**8.** Admission to a county fair is $8 for adults and $5 for children. Find the total cost of admission for 3 adults and 4 children.

F $20      H $47

G $44      J $116

## Sunil and Courtney in NET WORTH?

YOUR TURN! Can you help Courtney and Sunil choose?

# Algebraic Thinking

Read each question. Then, fill in the correct answer on the answer document provided by your teacher or on a sheet of paper.

**1.** Which of the following pairs of ratios is proportional?

  **A** 5 winners out of 20 participants
     6 winners out of 35 participants

  **B** 6 footballs out of 16 balls
     9 footballs out of 24 balls

  **C** 8 girls out of 20 students
     15 girls out of 35 students

  **D** 9 cars out of 26 automobiles
     24 cars out of 62 automobiles

**2.** Which percent represents the shaded portion of the model?

  **F** 20%      **H** 40%
  **G** 25%      **J** 75%

**3.** Jacob deposits $25 each week into his savings account. Which equation represents $t$, the total amount deposited in $w$ weeks?

  **A** $t = 25 + w$

  **B** $t = 25w$

  **C** $t = w - 25$

  **D** $t = \frac{w}{25}$

**4.** Use the ratio table to find the number of inches in 6 feet.

| Feet | 1 | 5 | 6 | 8 |
|------|---|---|---|---|
| Inches | 12 | 60 | ? | 96 |

  **F** 36 in.      **H** 72 in.
  **G** 48 in.      **J** 84 in.

**5.** If the pattern continues, which expression can be used to complete the table below?

| Position | Value of Term |
|----------|---------------|
| 1 | 6 |
| 2 | 8 |
| 3 | 10 |
| $n$ | ? |

  **A** $2n$

  **B** $4n + 2$

  **C** $2n + 4$

  **D** $n + 2$

**6.** An appliance technician charges $50 for a service call plus an additional $20 for each hour of labor. Which equation represents $c$, the cost in dollars for a service call that requires $h$ hours of labor?

  **F** $c = 20(h + 50)$

  **G** $c = 50(h + 20)$

  **H** $c = 50h + 20$

  **J** $c = 20h + 50$

**7.** Tamika surveyed her classmates and found that 12 out of 30 students had a dog for a pet. If there are 280 students in Tamika's school, predict how many students in the school have a dog, based on her survey.

  **A** 112

  **B** 124

  **C** 180

  **D** 216

I know the radius of the Earth.

It's about 3,958 miles from center of the Earth to the equator.

Radius

But we're not mole people. We can't tunnel through the Earth.

Welcome!

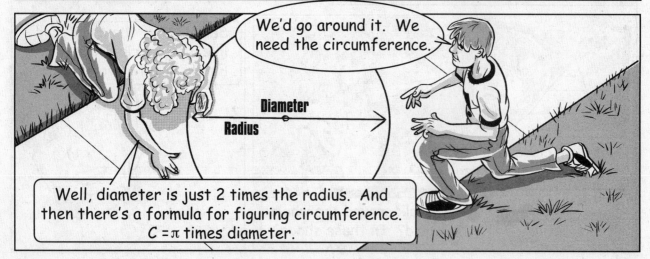

We'd go around it. We need the circumference.

Diameter

Radius

Well, diameter is just 2 times the radius. And then there's a formula for figuring circumference. $C = \pi$ times diameter.

# MEET ME THERE WITH TAMIKA, JONAS, & HILARY

# Geometry 3: Angles of Triangles

YOUR TURN!

CAN YOU SOLVE THE PROBLEM?

# Geometry

**Read each question. Then, fill in the correct answer on the answer document provided by your teacher or on a sheet of paper.**

**1.** Find the measure of ∠1.

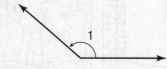

**A** 45°
**B** 90°
**C** 140°
**D** 180°

**2.** Which ordered pair names point *M*?

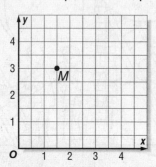

**F** (3, 1.5)    **H** (1, 3)
**G** (1.5, 3)   **J** (3, 1)

**3.** Which one of the following statements is always true concerning the relationships between the angles in quadrilaterals?

**A** All angles of a square are acute angles.
**B** All angles of a rhombus are right angles.
**C** Opposite angles of a parallelogram are congruent.
**D** Opposite angles of a trapezoid are congruent.

**4.** Which equation represents the relationship between the radius *r* and the diameter *d* of a circle?

**F** $d = 2r$        **H** $d = \frac{r}{2}$

**G** $r = 2d$        **J** $r = \frac{2}{d}$

**5.** Classify ∠*M* on triangle *MNQ*.

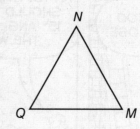

**A** acute
**B** obtuse
**C** right
**D** straight

**6.** Which of the following correctly displays the graph of point *R*(2.5, 1)?

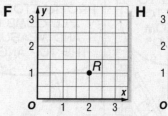

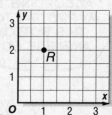

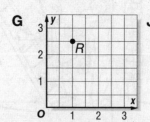

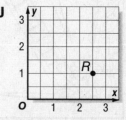

18

# Measurement 1: Circumference

OKAY, A 25-INCH TIRE REVOLVES *HOW MANY TIMES* OVER A DISTANCE OF 20 FEET?

WAIT--ALL OUR MEASUREMENTS SHOULD BE IN THE SAME UNITS, RIGHT?

SO 20 FEET EQUALS...

20 TIMES 12 INCHES IN A FOOT...

...240 INCHES.

GREAT. SO HOW MANY TIMES DOES THE *DISTANCE AROUND* THE TIRE--

--THE CIRCUMFERENCE.

RIGHT. HOW MANY TIMES DOES THAT GO INTO 240 INCHES?

BUT WE *DON'T KNOW* THE CIRCUMFERENCE, ONLY THE DIAMETER.

PI!

YEAH, WE CAN EAT DESSERT LATER. I WANT TO FIGURE THIS OUT FIRST.

NO, *PI TIMES THE DIAMETER* GIVES YOU THE CIRCUMFERENCE!

# Measurement 2: Converting Customary Units

ISABEL, TONISHA, AND CALVIN IN
## THE PLANE FACTS

Hey, check out the plane!

How many miles up do you think they are?

The last time I flew, we were at 35,000 feet for most of the flight.

We've now reached our cruising altitude of 35,000 feet and the seat belt sign has been turned off.

35,000 feet! That makes my head spin. I need it in miles!

I bet we can figure it out. We know what a mile is.

Yeah, 1,760 yards.

And there are 3 feet in 1 yard.

So, how many miles is 35,000 feet?

### YOUR TURN!
NOW IT'S UP TO YOU TO SOLVE THE PROBLEM.

22

# Measurement

Read each question. Then, fill in the correct answer on the answer document provided by your teacher or on a sheet of paper.

**1.** Which of the following is the most reasonable estimate for the length $x$ of the address label below?

Ms. Maya Levonshire
1280 Lakeside Drive
Houston, TX 77008

$\longleftarrow x \longrightarrow$

- **A** 1 ft
- **B** 6 in.
- **C** 4 cm
- **D** 10 mm

**2.** Latanya wants to put wallpaper border along the top of each wall of her bedroom. Her bedroom is 14 feet long and 12 feet wide. How many feet of wallpaper border will she need?

- **F** 26 ft
- **G** 48 ft
- **H** 52 ft
- **J** 168 ft

**3.** A plot of land is in the shape of a parallelogram with dimensions shown. Find the area of the plot.

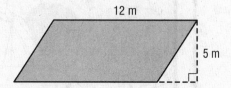

- **A** 17 m²
- **B** 30 m²
- **C** 34 m²
- **D** 60 m²

**4.** Use a protractor to find the measure of ∠1.

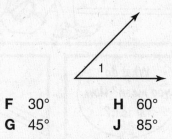

- **F** 30°   **H** 60°
- **G** 45°   **J** 85°

**5.** At 45 feet long, the whale shark is the world's largest fish. What is the length of the whale shark in yards?

- **A** 540 yd
- **B** 135 yd
- **C** 15 yd
- **D** 5 yd

**6.** Mario is participating in a 10-kilometer walk for a charity organization. At 11:15 A.M., he reads a sign which lets him know that there are only 250 meters to the finish line. At this time, how many meters has Mario already walked?

- **F** 750 m
- **G** 875 m
- **H** 8,750 m
- **J** 9,750 m

**7.** Jamal started studying for his science test at 7:25 P.M. and finished studying at 9:10 P.M. For how long did he study?

- **A** 1 h 15 min
- **B** 1 h 45 min
- **C** 2 h 15 min
- **D** 2 h 45 min

# NO TRICKS WITH KRISTIN AND ENRIQUE

OOH...

ENRIQUE! LISTEN UP! FUNBOX IS MAKING *12* NEW BOARDS.

NBOX BOARDS!

12 NEW BOARDS!

ALL NEW GRAPHICS!

ALL DIFFERENT! NEW GRAPHICS AND EVERYTHING.

TWELVE!?

*NAW, MAN. THAT CAN'T BE.*

## Statistics and Probability 1:
Sample Spaces and Tree Diagrams (*continued*)

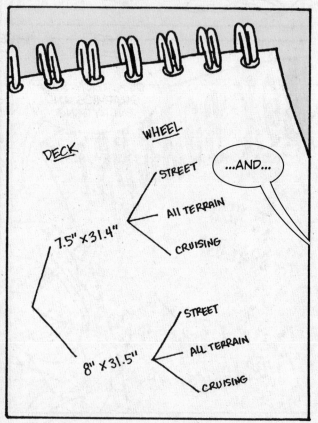

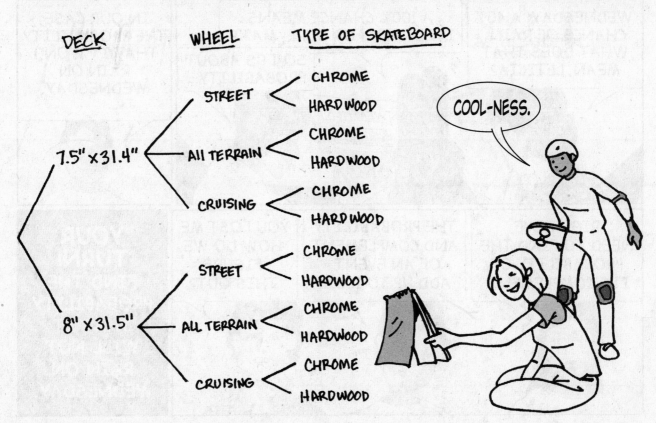

| DECK | WHEEL | TYPE OF SKATEBOARD |
|---|---|---|

**LETICIA, RUBEN & MATT IN RAIN OR SHINE**

TO MAKE PLANS FOR WEDNESDAY, WE NEED TO KNOW IF IT'S GOING TO RAIN OR SHINE.

MY CRYSTAL PAPERWEIGHT WON'T HELP.

LET'S CHECK THE NEWSPAPER.

| SUNDAY | MONDAY | TUESDAY | WEDNESDAY | THURSDAY |
|---|---|---|---|---|
| PARTLY CLOUDY | SUNNY | SHOWERS | SCATTERED SHOWERS | SUNNY |
| Chance of Rain: 35% | Chance of Rain: 10% | Chance of Rain: 70% | Chance of Rain: 45% | Chance of Rain: 5% |

'WEDNESDAY: A 45% CHANCE OF RAIN'. WHAT DOES THAT MEAN, LETICIA?

A 100% CHANCE MEANS IT'LL RAIN FOR SURE, MATT.

SO IT'S ABOUT PROBABILITY...

IN OUR CASE, THE PROBABILITY THAT IT WON'T RAIN ON WEDNESDAY.

RIGHT, WE NEED TO FIND THE PROBABILITY OF ITS COMPLEMENT.

THE PROBABILITY AND COMPLEMENT OF AN EVENT ADD UP TO 100%.

YOU LOST ME. HOW DO WE FIGURE THIS OUT?

**YOUR TURN!** FIND THE PROBABILITY THAT IT WILL NOT RAIN ON WEDNESDAY.

# Riding the Line

WITH ELENA, NICHOLAS, PAT, AND SARA

# PRACTICE On Your Own...

## Statistics and Probability

Read each question. Then, fill in the correct answer on the answer document provided by your teacher or on a sheet of paper.

**1.** The number of points David's basketball team scored in each of seven games is listed. Find the median of the set of data.

34, 28, 47, 24, 52, 38, 47

A 28     C 39
B 38     D 47

**2.** If the probability of randomly selecting a cherry lollipop from a package of lollipops is 35%, what is the probability of *not* randomly selecting a cherry lollipop from the same package?

F 15%     H 65%
G 35%     J 70%

**3.** The table shows the number of students in Mr. Hill's class who own each type of pet. What is the probability that a student chosen at random will own a bird?

| Pet | Number of Students |
|---|---|
| Dog | 27 |
| Cat | 16 |
| Bird | 10 |
| Other/None | 22 |

A $\frac{2}{15}$     C $\frac{1}{65}$
B $\frac{1}{7}$     D $\frac{2}{13}$

**4.** Which type of display would be the most appropriate for showing the change in a puppy's weight over the first several months after the puppy is born?

F bar graph     H line graph
G line plot     J stem-and-leaf plot

**5.** Which set of data is displayed in the graph?

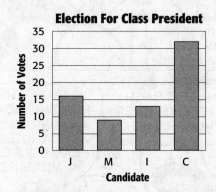

**A**

| Candidate | Votes |
|---|---|
| Juan | 14 |
| Mary | 10 |
| Isabel | 16 |
| Caleb | 28 |

**C**

| Candidate | Votes |
|---|---|
| Juan | 20 |
| Mary | 6 |
| Isabel | 10 |
| Caleb | 35 |

**B**

| Candidate | Votes |
|---|---|
| Juan | 13 |
| Mary | 9 |
| Isabel | 8 |
| Caleb | 32 |

**D**

| Candidate | Votes |
|---|---|
| Juan | 16 |
| Mary | 9 |
| Isabel | 13 |
| Caleb | 32 |

**6.** Which set lists all the possible outcomes of choosing the order in which Sara, Tad, and Jun play golf?

F {(Sara, Tad, Jun), (Sara, Jun, Tad), (Tad, Jun, Sara)}

G {(Sara, Tad, Jun), (Sara, Jun, Tad), (Tad, Sara, Jun), (Tad, Jun, Sara), (Jun, Sara, Tad), (Jun, Tad, Sara)}

H {(Sara, Tad, Jun), (Jun, Tad, Sara)}

J {(Jun, Sara, Tad), (Sara, Jun, Tad)}

RAMONA and TREVOR in MAKING THE MOVIE

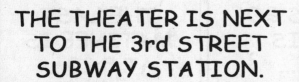

THE THEATER IS NEXT TO THE 3rd STREET SUBWAY STATION.

THE TRAIN LEAVES HARTFORD AVENUE EVERY 18 MINUTES.

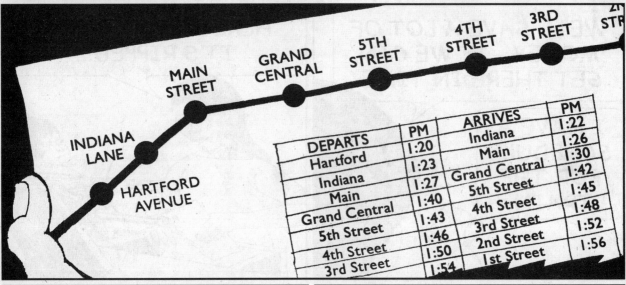

INDIANA LANE

HARTFORD AVENUE

MAIN STREET

GRAND CENTRAL

5TH STREET

4TH STREET

3RD STREET

| DEPARTS | PM | ARRIVES | PM |
|---|---|---|---|
| Hartford | 1:20 | Indiana | 1:22 |
| Indiana | 1:23 | Main | 1:26 |
| Main | 1:27 | Grand Central | 1:30 |
| Grand Central | 1:40 | 5th Street | 1:42 |
| 5th Street | 1:43 | 4th Street | 1:45 |
| 4th Street | 1:46 | 3rd Street | 1:48 |
| 3rd Street | 1:50 | 2nd Street | 1:52 |
| | 1:54 | 1st Street | 1:56 |

THE TRAIN LEAVES HARTFORD AT 1:20 PM.

ARRIVING AT 3RD STREET AT 1:48 PM.

HOW MUCH TIME IS BETWEEN 1:20 PM AND 1:48 PM?

48-20, OR 28 MINUTES.

LINDY AND CLEVELAND IN:
## "SOMETHING FISHY"

HEY LINDY, CHECK THIS ONE OUT!

LOOKS GOOD...

...BUT HOW MUCH WATER DOES IT HOLD? AND HOW MUCH GLASS WAS USED TO BUILD IT?

UMM...

THE TAG JUST LISTS THE DIMENSIONS: 32 INCHES LONG BY 15 INCHES WIDE BY 18 INCHES HIGH.

WELL, THAT'S A START. WE CAN USE THOSE MEASUREMENTS TO FIGURE OUT BOTH THE VOLUME AND THE SURFACE AREA.

BUT THE TOP OF THE TANK IS OPEN. DOES THAT AFFECT THE VOLUME OR THE SURFACE AREA?

UMM...

## YOUR TURN!

NOW IT'S UP TO YOU TO FIND HOW MUCH WATER THE TANK HOLDS AND HOW MUCH GLASS WAS USED TO BUILD IT!

SO THAT'LL BE WHAT-- SQUARE INCHES? CUBIC INCHES?

# Mathematical Reasoning

**Read each question. Then, fill in the correct answer on the answer document provided by your teacher or on a sheet of paper.**

**1.** The population of Tokyo, Japan, is about 34,997,300. The population of Shanghai, China, is about 12,759,000. Which of the following operations could be used to find how many more people live in Tokyo than Shanghai?

**A** addition

**B** subtraction

**C** multiplication

**D** division

**2.** If the pattern below is extended, which two figures would come next?

**3.** Julia has 5 bills that total $22. Which of the following could represent the bills?

**A** three $5 bills, two $1 bills

**B** one $10 bill, one $5 bill, seven $1 bills

**C** two $10 bills, two $1 bills

**D** one $10 bill, two $5 bills, two $1 bills

**4.** Ethan earns $125 per week working at a grocery store. At this rate, how much will he earn in 6 weeks?

**F** $500        **H** $875

**G** $750        **J** $1,000

**5.** Refer to the table below. How many days had a high temperature between 59°F and 69°F?

| Daily High Temperature (°F) | | | |
|---|---|---|---|
| 65 | 68 | 72 | 53 |
| 76 | 60 | 58 | 74 |
| 75 | 62 | 66 | 71 |

**A** 3        **C** 6

**B** 5        **D** 8

**6.** Which of the following is a correct method for finding the number of hours in 10 days?

**F** Add 10 and 24.

**G** Multiply 10 by 60.

**H** Multiply 10 by 24.

**J** Divide 24 by 10.

**7.** The table shows the number of each type of animal at a zoo.

| Animals at the Zoo | |
|---|---|
| Penguins | 18 |
| Otters | 12 |
| Manatees | 4 |
| Zebras | 8 |
| Monkeys | 32 |

Which type of display is most appropriate to compare the number of each type of animal?

**A** bar graph

**B** line graph

**C** line plot

**D** stem-and-leaf plot